Musical Writer's Planner

Your all-in-one workbook to brainstorm, develop, plan and calendar your new musical.

by Holly Reed

Owner & Chief Excitement Officer of MusicalWriters.com

Ultimate Musical Writer's Planner

_____

title of show

_____

writer name

_____

start date

table of contents

Welcome!

"A musical...
And nothing's as amazing as a musical!
With song and dance—and sweet romance
And happy endings happening by happenstance
Bright lights, stage fights, and a dazzling chorus
You wanna be great? Then you gotta create...
a musical!"

(from *Something Rotten!*)

. . . .

Welcome to the **Ultimate Musical Writer's Planner**—a central location to brainstorm, develop, plan, and calendar all of the things that go into creating a new musical.

When I wrote my first show, I poured through books, search online articles, and listen to countless podcasts to find help with both the creative aspects of writing and the development and producing side. My many notes and ideas were scattered among legal pads, journals, and random scraps of paper.

I thought, "Wouldn't it be nice to have one place to keep all of this information together so I can look back at my early ideas, plans, contacts and milestones?" And the idea for the Ultimate Musical Writer's Planner was born.

This planner wasn't intended to be a "how-to" book on writing musicals. It was more designed to be a tool to help codify your ideas. You'll find guides on outlining story structure and character development, charts for determining vocal ranges and rhyme patterns, checklists for readings and marketing, goal planning sheets, a monthly planning calendar, and more.

Writing a musical isn't easy, and it can take years of work to successfully move it from idea to stage. Hopefully, this planner will help you feel less overwhelmed and trigger some important ideas. It may even become a treasured memento of the journey.

So glad you're getting started. I can't wait to hear of your progress. Have fun!

Holly Reed

. . . .

SECTION ONE

getting
started

getting started

So you've got an idea for a musical. A small little seed that has taken root in the creative, fertile soil of your mind.

Congratulations! You're on your way!

Just like building a house, you want your show to start off on a solid foundation. The shape of the house determines its foundational footprint—every one is different. So we're going to look at a few important considerations when preparing to create your musical's foundation.

Here's what this section will cover:

· Helpful tools
· Finding collaborators
· Determining your vision
· Creating a mood board

Glad you're here. Let's get started!

helpful tools

When you're starting to write a musical, it will help to have a few tools at-the-ready so you don't have to interrupt your creative juices once they start flowing. Here are a few I suggest:

Index Cards (multi-colors work great!)
Index cards are great for plotting out your story. Use various colors for characters, locations, songs, plot points, etc.

A variety of colored pens and pencils

Computer + Writing Software
Recommended: FinalDraft

Rhyming Dictionary
A rhyming dictionary, either hard-copy or online, can prove extremely helpful in broadening options for lyrics.
(Also try RhymeZone.com)

Voice Recording App
This is my #1 recommended tool. When you have an idea (lyric, melody, character, dialogue, scene, etc.), record it! You'll thank yourself later!

Voice Memos App (iPhone)
Voice Recorder (Google Play)

Your beverage of choice!

finding collaborators

Most likely, you are going to want to write your musical with a collaborator. Theatre is a collaborative industry, and learning to bravely share ideas, respectfully listen to others, and discern which battles to fight will dramatically help you in the long run.

You have a wheelhouse—a lane—that you know and feel comfortable in. That's where you should focus your time and effort. Your collaborator should provide a complimentary skill set.

Use these boxes to honestly evaluate what you bring to the table, and what you're looking for in a collaborator.

MY TECHNICAL SKILLS

MY STRENGTHS

MY WEAKNESSES

WHAT I NEED

collaborator checklist

Have someone in mind that you'd like a potential collaboration partnership with?
A collaboration is like a marriage, and the musical is like a child. Don't enter that relationship lightly. The points below, suggested by Tom Jones, Julian Woolford, and David Spencer are wise to consider before starting your project together.

☐ "Find someone whose taste in shows is similar to yours. If you consistently find that you are excited, or bored, by the same shows, it is a good sign. If you consistently disagree, you will probably have trouble working together."*

☐ "Have clearly distinct talents. While you can share and brainstorm together, make clearly defined lines on who is in charge of what."*

☐ "Find someone to whom you may convey your honest feelings. Even harder, find someone you respect enough to accept criticism from."*

☐ "Don't get too personally close. Keep your partnership businesslike. Don't socialize together too much if you can help it. If you have any success, you will be thrown together all of the time. Keep space. Don't wear out each other's welcome."*

☐ "Make decisions together. On matters of business and artistic policy, you must agree. If you can't, you shouldn't be partners. In the domain of the other person's talent, you have to let that person have the final say."*

☐ "Find someone whose work you like and respect, and they like and respect your work."**

☐ "Be temperamentally compatible."**

☐ "Do a trial run. Write one song or a 10-minute musical together."**

☐ "Discuss your working practices and habits."**

☐ "Remember, what's really at stake here is your psychological health. The work we do is so personal, and we are so exposed while going through the birth process, that we need to be a part of a support system that will nourish and encourage our efforts and enthusiasm as much as possible."***

☐ "What's important is that both parties feel that they're respected partners in the gestation process."***

☐ "Never expose your disagreements in any way that lets anyone think that your loyalties can be divided. If an opportunistic director, producer or star senses that she can play one of you against the other, she will 85% of the time. And then you might as well draw your own chalk outline and fit yourself for a toe tag. Because but for the lying down, you're already a corpse. And so's the show."***

☐ "Never let anyone in a position of power—director, producer, star, anyone—speak to you off the record or confidentially about your partner." ***

*Tom Jones (**Making Musicals**), **Julian Woolford (**How Musicals Work**),
***David Spencer (**The Musical Theater Writer's Survival Guide**)

· ·

potential collaborators

You can search for potential collaborators at networking events, in shared online and in-person classes, by viewing others' websites, by attending festivals, from recommendations, and several other ways. Meet someone you'd like to consider? Record their information here.

NAME

EMAIL

SKILLS

PHONE

WEBSITE

SHOWS

THOUGHTS ON COLLABORATING

NAME

EMAIL

SKILLS

PHONE

WEBSITE

SHOWS

THOUGHTS ON COLLABORATING

NAME

EMAIL

SKILLS

PHONE

WEBSITE

SHOWS

THOUGHTS ON COLLABORATING

potential collaborators

NAME

EMAIL

SKILLS

PHONE

WEBSITE

SHOWS

THOUGHTS ON COLLABORATING

NAME

EMAIL

SKILLS

PHONE

WEBSITE

SHOWS

THOUGHTS ON COLLABORATING

NAME

EMAIL

SKILLS

PHONE

WEBSITE

SHOWS

THOUGHTS ON COLLABORATING

preparation & vision

SOME OF MY FAVORITE MUSICALS ARE:

**WHAT ASPECTS OF THOSE MUSICALS
DO YOU WANT TO INCLUDE IN YOUR MUSICAL?**

preparation & vision

I WANT MY MUSICAL TO BE:

I DON'T WANT MY MUSICAL TO BE:

WHEN MY AUDIENCE LEAVES THE THEATER, I WANT THEM TO FEEL:

brain dump #1

Use this page to jot down everything you know about your musical this far. Fill this page as much as possible with thoughts on characters, story, settings, themes, emotions, genres, music styles, etc. Don't edit your thoughts before you put them down. Just write! Doodle if necessary, draw pictures if it helps. Just "dump" everything that's in your brain right now about your musical

MY MUSICAL'S
mood board

Creating a mood board for your musical can help provide a visual feel for your show. Below are some examples of images to collect.

COLORS   **CHARACTERS**   **CLOTHING**

THEME

SOUND   **PROPS**   **EMOTIONS**

TIME PERIOD   **WEATHER**   **LOCATION**

You can create a digital mood board by copying and pasting found images into software like Powerpoint, Word, Apple Pages, Photoshop, etc.

Online tools for creating moodboards:

Pinterest.com · *Canva* · *Adobe Spark* · *Milanote*

mood board

Here's a sample mood board I did for our holiday show, "Come Find Me."

mood board

Now it's your turn. Cut, paste, tape, draw and doodle to your heart's content!

the book & story structure

story structure

While there are no set rules for creating musicals, having a road map to follow can be very beneficial to create a story that is meaningful, entertaining and satisfying to audiences.

In the following pages, we'll be using the story arc known as the Hero's Journey. This story structure is as old as time. From *Oedipus Rex* to *Harry Potter*, so many narratives follow this pattern that it's ingrained in our cultural DNA today. Your libretto (script plus lyrics) may not follow

this form exactly, but it is a good exercise to go through to define important moments in your story.

Be prepared to spend some time in this section. In fact, I'm suggesting that you take an entire month to do the 30-day brainstorm that's included. It will give you time to really let the ideas simmer, plus it will allow you to explore your story in bite-size pieces.

Need an example? Click here to see how 6 iconic movies follow the hero's journey.

OUTLINING
the hero's journey

The monomyth, or the Hero's Journey, is the common template used for storytelling that involves a hero who goes on an adventure, and in a decisive crisis wins a victory, and then comes home changed or transformed. This is the basic story arc you're going to use to develop your story.

story brainstorm

Habit, pattern, routine...call it what you will, but having a PLAN will help you be a better writer. Let's take 30 days to work your ideas and see what happens!

DAY 1

1. What is the everyday, normal world that your Protagonist lives in? Time? Setting?

2. What do you think your audience will find interesting about your Protagonist?

3. What is unique about your Protagonist?

DAY 2

1. What other characters does the Protagonist interact with?

2. Who is the Antagonist?

3. While the Protagonist has been living in their "normal world," what has the Antagonist been doing?

DAY 3

1. What problem will you introduce to your Protagonist's life?

2. What is your Protagonist's first reaction to this change?

3. What is the Protagonist's plan for dealing with the new change?

DAY 4

1. What is the Protagonist's flaw?

2. How is the Protagonist's flaw making it harder for him/her to deal with this change?

3. How is the Protagonist's problem worse than he/she realizes?

4. What resources does the Protagonist have that he/she can use to address the problem?

DAY 5

1. What is the biggest obstacle to the Protagonist fixing the problem?

2. How are the Protagonist's problems affecting other people in his/her life?

3. How is the Antagonist contributing to the problem?

DAY 6

1. What causes the situation to blow up?

2. Who is involved in this heightened conflict situation?

3. What are the results of this blow-up?

DAY 7

1. What new territory must the Protagonist brave in order to solve his/her problem?

2. Why doesn't he/she want to go there?

3. How is the Antagonist responsible for making the situation worse?

4. Does the Protagonist have an Ally or Mentor who helps them? Who are they?

DAY 8

1. What is the "new world" the Protagonist is now in? How does it look different from the "normal world" he/she started in?

2. What does the Protagonist have to sacrifice to enter this new world?

3. Are there any forces trying to stop the Protagonist from entering this new world?

4. How does the Protagonist work to overcome these opposing forces?

5. How is the Antagonist hindering the Protagonist from entering the new world?

DAY 9

1. If a Sage, Mentor, or Ally is present, how did he/she meet the Protagonist?

2. In what ways is there conflict between the Protagonist and the Ally?

3. Why must the Protagonist and the Ally work together?

4. How is the Antagonist working against the Ally?

DAY 10

1. What new experiences is the Protagonist having in this new world?

2. What has the Protagonist learned that will help him fight the Antagonist later?

3. What is the Antagonist doing behind-the-scenes to hinder the Protagonist?

story brainstorm

DAY 11

1. What new trouble does the Protagonist get into?

2. How does the Protagonist's flaw make it more likely that he/she will get into trouble, or harder to get out of trouble once he/she is in it?

3. How does the Ally contribute to the trouble or try to stop it from happening?

4. Does the Protagonist realize his/her flaw and how it is causing problems?

5. How does the Ally express his/her awareness of the Protagonist's flaw?

DAY 12

1. How do the Protagonist and Ally disagree about solving their predicament?

2. How do the Protagonist and Ally resolve their differences?

3. How does working together (or not) cause the Protagonist and Ally to change their opinions of each other?

4. What is the Antagonist up to at this point?

DAY 13

1. What narrow escape has just happened that now raises the stakes even more?

2. How does the Protagonist's unfamiliarity with the new world make this even more difficult?

3. What is the current working relationship of the Protagonist and the Ally?

4. What makes the Protagonist recognize his/her flaw?

DAY 14

1. What is the new plan for defeating the Antagonist?

2. How are the higher stakes making the battle against the Antagonist even harder?

3. How is this difficulty affecting the relationship between the Protagonist and Ally?

4. How is the Protagonist compensating for his/her flaw? Is it working?

5. What is the Antagonist's plan for resisting the efforts of the Protagonist?

story brainstorm

DAY 15

1. What new resources and allies has the Protagonist gained?

2. What obstacles are looming in the distance that the Protagonist will likely face?

3. Is the Protagonist aware of these obstacles? What is his/her plan for overcoming them?

4. What is the Antagonist doing while the Protagonist is gaining allies and courage?

5. Is the Ally a part of the Protagonist's allies at this point?

DAY 16

1. What do the Protagonist and Ally agree on?

2. What do the Protagonist and Ally disagree on?

3. What is the Protagonist doing to overcome his/her flaw? Is it working?

4. How have the Protagonist and Ally decided to move forward together?

story brainstorm

DAY 17

1. How does the Protagonist come directly into conflict with the Antagonist?

2. How does the Protagonist's flaw throw a wrench in the plan?

3. How do the Protagonist and/or Ally compensate for the problem caused by the flaw?

4. How is the Protagonist worse off after this encounter?

story brainstorm

DAY 18

1. What important thing did the Protagonist and Ally learn after their recent failure?

2. How do they adjust their plan moving forward?

3. How did the recent failure create even more problems?

4. What is the Antagonist doing in the aftermath of the recent conflict and seeming victory?

story brainstorm

DAY 19

1. What is the Protagonist's new plan of attack in getting what they want?

2. What problems does that new plan face?

3. What progress is made using the new plan?

4. How is the Protagonist's flaw still a problem?

DAY 20

1. How are the newest problems affecting the relationship between the Protagonist and Ally/ allies?

2. What is the Protagonist now doing differently that is helping compensate for and overcome his/her flaw?

3. What doubts does the Ally have in the Protagonist?

4. What doubts does the Protagonist have in him/herself?

story brainstorm

DAY 21

1. What new progress is made against the Antagonist's forces or to gain the Protagonist's want?

2. If there is another heightened conflict or skirmish with the Antagonist, who wins?

3. What new is gained or learned from this battle?

story brainstorm

DAY 22

1. How have the circumstances changed since the Protagonist (and Ally) first made a plan? Is there something new he/she wasn't aware of?

2. What secret weapon does the Antagonist have up his/her sleeve?

3. If made aware, how does the Protagonist react to the news of this secret weapon?

4. What is the current relationship between the Protagonist and Ally?

5. How are the current events affecting that relationship?

story brainstorm

DAY 23

1. How does the Antagonist turn the tables in a new, monumental battle?

2. What desperate measures does the Protagonist take?

3. What triggers the Protagonist's flaw to resurface? How does this flaw affect the battle?

4. How does the relationship between the Protagonist and Ally affect the battle?

5. How does the battle affect the relationship between the Protagonist and Ally?

DAY 24

1. How does the Antagonist defeat the Protagonist in a dramatic way?

2. How does this defeat make it seem like all is lost for the Protagonist ever succeeding in achieving his/her goal?

3. How does this defeat cause the Protagonist to struggle even more with his/her flaw?

4. How does this defeat affect the relationship between the Protagonist and Ally?

DAY 25

1. How does the Protagonist's flaw contribute to his/her loss of faith?

2. How does the Ally react to the Protagonist's gloom?

3. What is the Antagonist doing while the Protagonist is down?

story brainstorm

DAY 26

1. How does the Protagonist regain his/her determination to achieve his/her goal?

2. What happens to make the Protagonist think he/she has a chance to win?

3. What is the new plan?

4. How is the Ally involved in the new plan?

5. How does the Protagonist (and Ally if involved) make preparations for the new plan?

DAY 27

1. What obstacles will the Protagonist face in this final battle?

2. How is the Protagonist prepared for these obstacles?

3. How does the Protagonist overcome the obstacles?

4. What does the Protagonist lose in the process?

story brainstorm

DAY 28

1. What toll is this final battle taking on the Protagonist, Ally, and any of their allies?

2. What toll is this final battle taking on the Antagonist?

3. What surprises does the Antagonist have prepared?

4. How does the Protagonist's defeat seem all but certain?

5. How does the Protagonist's flaw come into play?

DAY 29

1. What is the moment when the Protagonist and Antagonist face off in a final battle?

2. What does the Protagonist sacrifice in his/her attempt to defeat the Antagonist?

3. How does the Protagonist succeed in overcoming his/her flaw once and for all?

4. How does this final battle affect the relationship between the Antagonist and Ally?

5. What does the Protagonist gain as a result of this final battle? Is it his/her original want, or a completely new one?

story brainstorm

DAY 30

1. What is the "New Normal World" of the Protagonist after the victory?

2. Where does the Antagonist fit in this new normal world?

3. Where does the Ally fit in this new normal world?

4. How has the final battle changed the Protagonist?

5. What overarching theme do you want your audience to walk away with as a result of hearing this story? How can they be changed?

brain dump #2

You've made some progress on your characters, plot, story and theme.
It's time for another Brain Dump! Fill this page on the high points of what
comes to mind now that you've worked through the 30 Day Brainstorm.

OUTLINING
your hero's journey

Now that you've thoroughly explored your story, use this to plot your Protagonist's journey. Your story arc doesn't have to fit this format exactly, but you should be able to fill out most boxes and the events should occur roughly in this order.

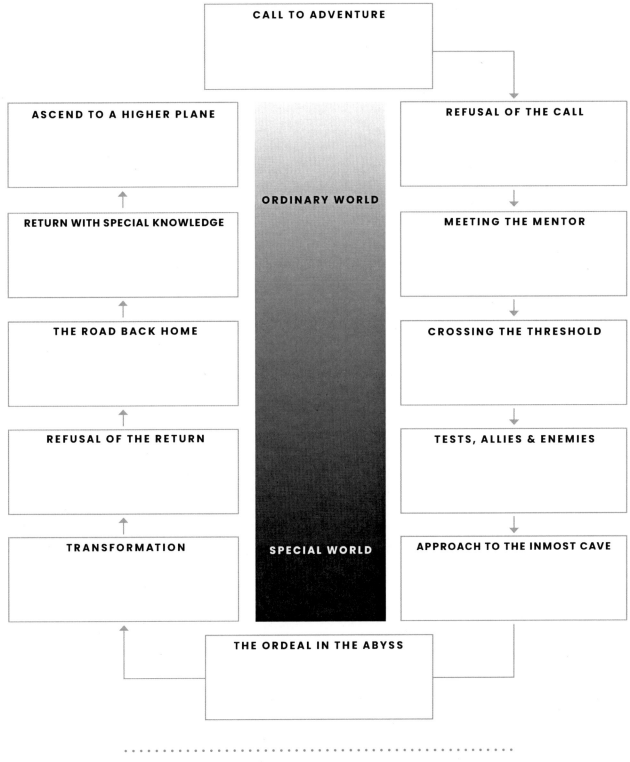

CALL TO ADVENTURE

ASCEND TO A HIGHER PLANE

REFUSAL OF THE CALL

RETURN WITH SPECIAL KNOWLEDGE

ORDINARY WORLD

MEETING THE MENTOR

THE ROAD BACK HOME

CROSSING THE THRESHOLD

REFUSAL OF THE RETURN

TESTS, ALLIES & ENEMIES

TRANSFORMATION

SPECIAL WORLD

APPROACH TO THE INMOST CAVE

THE ORDEAL IN THE ABYSS

main setting

MY STORY TAKES PLACE IN/AT   **HOW IS THIS SETTING UNIQUE?**

HOW DO MY MAIN CHARACTERS RELATE TO THIS SETTING?

PROTAGONIST

ANTAGONIST

OTHER

secondary setting

MY STORY TAKES PLACE IN/AT　　　**HOW IS THIS SETTING UNIQUE?**

HOW DO MY MAIN CHARACTERS RELATE TO THIS SETTING?

PROTAGONIST

ANTAGONIST

OTHER

other settings

List any other major or minor settings in the world of your show. These can be specific places within a larger setting, such as a bedroom in the Protagonist's home, a bench in Central Park, etc.

character development

character development

"It is not enough, in your study of a man, to know if he is rude, polite, religious, atheistic, moral, degenerate. You must know why."

~*Lajos Egri,* **The Art of Dramatic Writing***.*

To create a great a great experience in the theater, you must create vibrant, compelling, and likable characters.

It's important to also know not only WHAT they are going to do as it relates to moving your plot forward, but WHY they will do it. That all depends on WHO they are and HOW they became that way.

Taking the time to develop your characters will not only help you keep their decisions and motivations consistent throughout the show, it will also help clarify their character voice. This voice also needs to be consistent with how they speak, how they think, the words they choose to use, the way they sing, and the way they respond to others.

If you're not familiar with the Enneagram, let me encourage you to become familiar with this unique personality test. Take the test on yourself (it will be eye opening!) and then study the other personalities types and how your characters fall into each category. It's also interesting to explore how the various personalities react to each other. That can be super helpful in developing potential conflict situations!

For more about the Enneagram, read **The Road Back to You** *by Ian Cron.*

INTRODUCTION TO
my characters

Fill in the blanks below with your first thoughts about your character.

_____

Character Name

AGE GENDER RACE CAREER

PERSONALITY STRENGTHS FEARS

KNOWN FLAW UNKNOWN FLAW SECRET

SUPERPOWER WARDROBE HOBBIES

CLASS/STATUS LOCATION EDUCATION

VALUES SUCCESSES REGRETS

· ·
MusicalWriters.com • The Ultimate Musical Writer's Planner

61

INTRODUCTION TO
my characters

Fill in the blanks below with your first thoughts about your character.

_____
Character Name

AGE	GENDER	RACE	CAREER

PERSONALITY   **STRENGTHS**   **FEARS**

KNOWN FLAW   **UNKNOWN FLAW**   **SECRET**

SUPERPOWER   **WARDROBE**   **HOBBIES**

CLASS/STATUS   **LOCATION**   **EDUCATION**

VALUES   **SUCCESSES**   **REGRETS**

INTRODUCTION TO
my characters

Fill in the blanks below with your first thoughts about your character.

_____

Character Name

AGE	GENDER	RACE	CAREER

PERSONALITY   **STRENGTHS**   **FEARS**

KNOWN FLAW   **UNKNOWN FLAW**   **SECRET**

SUPERPOWER   **WARDROBE**   **HOBBIES**

CLASS/STATUS   **LOCATION**   **EDUCATION**

VALUES   **SUCCESSES**   **REGRETS**

INTRODUCTION TO
my characters

Fill in the blanks below with your first thoughts about your character.

_____

Character Name

| AGE | GENDER | RACE | CAREER |

| PERSONALITY | STRENGTHS | FEARS |

| KNOWN FLAW | UNKNOWN FLAW | SECRET |

| SUPERPOWER | WARDROBE | HOBBIES |

| CLASS/STATUS | LOCATION | EDUCATION |

| VALUES | SUCCESSES | REGRETS |

INTRODUCTION TO
my characters

Fill in the blanks below with your first thoughts about your character.

_____

Character Name

AGE   GENDER   RACE   CAREER

PERSONALITY   STRENGTHS   FEARS

KNOWN FLAW   UNKNOWN FLAW   SECRET

SUPERPOWER   WARDROBE   HOBBIES

CLASS/STATUS   LOCATION   EDUCATION

VALUES   SUCCESSES   REGRETS

character mood board

This is a page for you to build a visual view of your character. Know an actor who would be perfect for this role? Paste their photo on this page. Other ideas are emotions, colors, costume possibilities, personal props, etc.

_____

Character Name

character mood board

This is a page for you to build a visual view of your character. Know an actor who would be perfect for this role? Paste their photo on this page. Other ideas are emotions, colors, costume possibilities, personal props, etc.

_____

Character Name

character mood board

This is a page for you to build a visual view of your character. Know an actor who would be perfect for this role? Paste their photo on this page. Other ideas are emotions, colors, costume possibilities, personal props, etc.

_____

Character Name

character mood board

This is a page for you to build a visual view of your character. Know an actor who would be perfect for this role? Paste their photo on this page. Other ideas are emotions, colors, costume possibilities, personal props, etc.

_____

Character Name

character mood board

This is a page for you to build a visual view of your character. Know an actor who would be perfect for this role? Paste their photo on this page. Other ideas are emotions, colors, costume possibilities, personal props, etc.

_____

Character Name

character mood board

This is a page for you to build a visual view of your character. Know an actor who would be perfect for this role? Paste their photo on this page. Other ideas are emotions, colors, costume possibilities, personal props, etc.

_____
Character Name

character profile

Use this sheet to fill out more solid information on each of your characters based on your character brainstorm, your 30-day brainstorm, and your story outline.

NAME:

ROLE:

WANT:

AGE: _____

NEED:

GENDER: _____

This character has been shaped by the following past events:

This character's main flaw:

How do other characters view this character?

Other important details (Physical appearance, quirks, personality traits, beliefs, cultural background, possessions, and special skills/abilities):

How does this character change by the end of the show?

character profile

Use this sheet to fill out more solid information on each of your characters based on your character brainstorm, your 30-day brainstorm, and your story outline.

NAME:

ROLE:

WANT:

AGE: _____
NEED:

GENDER: _____

This character has been shaped by the following past events:

This character's main flaw:

How do other characters view this character?

Other important details (Physical appearance, quirks, personality traits, beliefs, cultural background, possessions, and special skills/abilities):

How does this character change by the end of the show?

character profile

Use this sheet to fill out more solid information on each of your characters based on your character brainstorm, your 30-day brainstorm, and your story outline.

NAME:

ROLE:

WANT:

AGE: _____

NEED:

GENDER: _____

This character has been shaped by the following past events:

This character's main flaw: *How do other characters view this character?*

Other important details (Physical appearance, quirks, personality traits, beliefs, cultural background, possessions, and special skills/abilities):

How does this character change by the end of the show?

character profile

Use this sheet to fill out more solid information on each of your characters based on your character brainstorm, your 30-day brainstorm, and your story outline.

NAME:

ROLE:

WANT:

AGE: _____

NEED:

GENDER: _____

This character has been shaped by the following past events:

This character's main flaw: *How do other characters view this character?*

Other important details (Physical appearance, quirks, personality traits, beliefs, cultural background, possessions, and special skills/abilities):

How does this character change by the end of the show?

character profile

Use this sheet to fill out more solid information on each of your characters based on your character brainstorm, your 30-day brainstorm, and your story outline.

NAME:

ROLE:

WANT:

AGE: _____

NEED:

GENDER: _____

This character has been shaped by the following past events:

This character's main flaw: *How do other characters view this character?*

Other important details (Physical appearance, quirks, personality traits, beliefs, cultural background, possessions, and special skills/abilities):

How does this character change by the end of the show?

character profile

Use this sheet to fill out more solid information on each of your characters based on your character brainstorm, your 30-day brainstorm, and your story outline.

NAME:

ROLE:

WANT:

AGE: _____

NEED:

GENDER: _____

This character has been shaped by the following past events:

This character's main flaw:

How do other characters view this character?

Other important details (Physical appearance, quirks, personality traits, beliefs, cultural background, possessions, and special skills/abilities):

How does this character change by the end of the show?

whew.
you did it!

You've done the homework.

Now it's time to write your script!

writing the script

writing the script

Congratulations! You have done some really great work on your story and character development. This is a massive milestone in creating a new musical.

At this point, your characters should be clear, your story arc mapped out, and the plot points clarified. From here, the writing can flow nicely.

Now it's time to dive into actually writing the script.

On the following pages, you'll find worksheets on setting up the major 7 plot points, creating your scenes, how to format correctly, how to song spot, and a 10 question evaluation to help you be your own "script doctor."

While you'll actually be writing the script *outside* this planner, keep it handy so you can refer to your notes for ideas and structure.

It's time to dig in. You can do it!

seven plot points

The 7 Plot Points are a concept used in Steve Cuden's book, **Beating Broadway**,
and are a streamlined version of the Hero's Journey.
Use this chart to create the high points that your musical will cover.

NORMAL WORLD
*Where the story starts. The "everyday"
world in which your Protagonist lives.*

INCITING INCIDENT
*An event that forces the
Protagonist down a new road
and establishes his goal.*

POINT OF NO RETURN
*A decision the Protagonist makes
forcing him/her to leave everything in
pursuit of the new goal.*

MIDPOINT BEGINS
*The protagonist jumps hurdles
necessary to achieve his new goal.*

INTERMISSION

MIDPOINT CONTINUES
*The protagonist continues his fight
but begins to grow weary from the
growing obstacles.*

THE BIG GLOOM
*The Protagonist is overwhelmed and
thinks he/she is going to fail.*

CLIMAX INTO RESOLUTION
*A moment of inspiration in which the
Protagonist discovers a way to succeed
after all.*

NEW NORMAL
*The Protagonist has reached the
resolution of his/her goal, learning
something in the result.*

scene summary

Try to distill each scene down to one or two sentences. Where does the scene take place? What main characters are in each scene? What is happening? What are the obstacles and outcomes, conflicts and resolutions?

Act ___ / Scene ___ : _____

_____

Act ___ / Scene ___ : _____

_____

Act ___ / Scene ___ : _____

_____

Act ___ / Scene ___ : _____

_____

Act ___ / Scene ___ : _____

_____

Act ___ / Scene ___ : _____

_____

Act ___ / Scene ___ : _____

_____

Act ___ / Scene ___ : _____

_____

Act ___ / Scene ___ : _____

_____

scene summary

Act   / Scene   :
_____

_____

Act   / Scene   :
_____

_____

Act   / Scene   :
_____

_____

Act   / Scene   :
_____

_____

Act   / Scene   :
_____

_____

Act   / Scene   :
_____

_____

Act   / Scene   :
_____

_____

Act   / Scene   :
_____

_____

Act   / Scene   :
_____

_____

Act   / Scene   :
_____

_____

scene summary

Act   / Scene   :

_____

Act   / Scene   :

_____

Act   / Scene   :

_____

Act   / Scene   :

_____

Act   / Scene   :

_____

Act   / Scene   :

_____

Act   / Scene   :

_____

Act   / Scene   :

_____

Act   / Scene   :

_____

Act   / Scene   :

_____

I-1-1

(SCENE HEADING) ACT ONE - SCENE 1

(SCENE INFO) THE LIBRARY. JUNE 12, 2004. EARLY EVENING.

(Action or Stage Directions) Here is where you will set up the beginning of your scenes and give necessary information.

This format is based on The Dramatists Guild of America's suggested musical format.

The font is Times New Roman 12pt.

BILL stands ready to help you.

(CHARACTER) BILL
(parenthetical)
(Dialogue) This is the dialogue for all of your character's great lines.

This is stage action not reliant on dialogue.

JANE
(giggles)
Oh Bill, you say the sweetest things.

Song: "1. MY LYRIC SONG"

(She sings.)
(LYRICS) ARE IN ALL CAPS
USE SHIFT + ENTER/RETURN TO
SEPARATE LINES
STANZAS ARE SEPARATED BY A BLANK LINE
USE SHIFT + ENTER/RETURN TWICE
TO INSERT A NEW STANZA

BILL
That was a great song, but I'm sure the writer will use this template and write some better songs. Hopefully you'll still think I'm sweet by the end.

JANE
I guess we'll have to wait and see, but this template should get the writer on its way.

5/24/19

For a full guide on formatting your script,
*see "**Formatting Guide for Musical Scripts**" on MusicalWriters.com.*

the magic ten

SELLING POINTS OF ANY GOOD SHOW

In *The Musical Theatre Writer's Survival Guide*, David Spencer encourages writers to
consider these common selling points that occur in most successful musicals.
Ready to see how your show checks out?
Rate where your show falls in accomplishing each of these points.

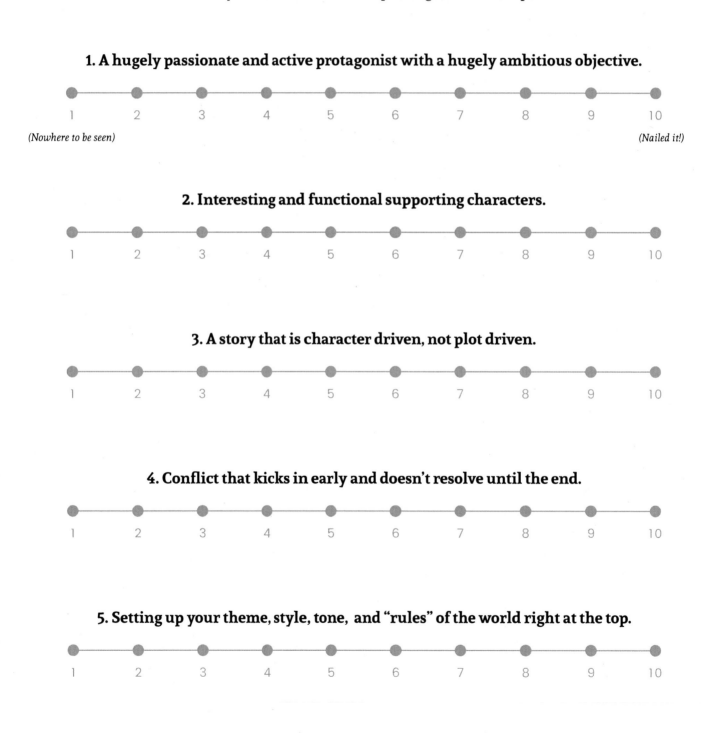

1. A hugely passionate and active protagonist with a hugely ambitious objective.

1   2   3   4   5   6   7   8   9   10

(Nowhere to be seen)   *(Nailed it!)*

2. Interesting and functional supporting characters.

1   2   3   4   5   6   7   8   9   10

3. A story that is character driven, not plot driven.

1   2   3   4   5   6   7   8   9   10

4. Conflict that kicks in early and doesn't resolve until the end.

1   2   3   4   5   6   7   8   9   10

5. Setting up your theme, style, tone, and "rules" of the world right at the top.

1   2   3   4   5   6   7   8   9   10

the magic ten
SELLING POINTS OF ANY GOOD SHOW

6. An underlying dramatic theme—what are you saying BEYOND the story?

1   2   3   4   5   6   7   8   9   10

(Nowhere to be seen)   *(Nailed it!)*

7. Plant seeds that track well and have payoffs later.

1   2   3   4   5   6   7   8   9   10

8. An otherwordly or interesting setting/location - places far away from everyday life.

1   2   3   4   5   6   7   8   9   10

9. Sustainable believability in the universe you're creating.

1   2   3   4   5   6   7   8   9   10

10. The ending restores balance. Somehow reward the audience for taking the journey!

1   2   3   4   5   6   7   8   9   10

Now total your points. What's your current grade?

SCORE:

Not happy with your grade? Do some rewrites, then retest!

SECTION FIVE

music &
songwriting

music & songwriting

A musical is not just a play with music. If the music were lifted from a musical, the story should be unidentifiable. That's because the songs play an integral role in the narrative. The music has the responsibility of moving the action forward and expressing the innermost thoughts of the characters.

Music also allows the story to reach both sides of our brain at the same time, our logical, storytelling side as well as our emotional side. The songs in your show create a visceral experience that is hard to explain, but impossible to miss. Whether through vivacious production numbers, delightful charm songs, passionate ballads, or angry rants, the music tells the tale.

Use this section to consider what and where songs should occur in your story. As you brainstorm on lyric and melody ideas, also remember to keep performers' vocal ranges in mind.

song spotting

Song spotting is deciding where the songs will be placed.
As you work through your script, consider which moments are "larger than life"
or are highly emotional. Those are typically the best moments to musicalize.
The chart below can help in finding key stages that contain songs.

HERO'S JOURNEY	7 PLOT POINTS	SONG TYPE*	EXAMPLE
The Ordinary World	Normal World	Opening Number	"Welcome to the Renaissance" *Something Rotten*
Call to Adventure	Inciting Incident	"I Want" Song	"Corner of the Sky" *Pippin*
Refusal of the Call			
Meeting the Mentor		Teaching Song	"Right Hand Man" *Hamilton*
Crossing the Threshold	Point of No Return		"Step One" *Kinky Boots*
Tests, Allies & Enemies	Midpoint	Buddy Song, Second Couples, Villains	"Be Our Guest" *Beauty & The Beast*
Preparation for the Supreme Ordeal	Midpoint		
The Supreme Ordeal (metamorphosis)		Curtain, Act One	"Defying Gravity" *Wicked*
INTERMISSION			
Reward		Act Two Opener	"God, That's Good!" *Sweeney Todd*
The Road Back	The Big Gloom		"Words Fail" *Dear Evan Hansen*
The Final Conflict	Climax into Resolution	11 o'clock Number	"Rose's Turn" *Gypsy*
Return to Stability	New Normal	Finale	"You Can't Stop the Beat" *Hairspray*

*For more information on song types, read **"The Secret Life of the American Musical"** by Jack Viertel.*

song spotting

Now fill in your ideas for songs.
Note that you may have more than one song for each plot point.

HERO'S JOURNEY	7 PLOT POINTS	SONG IDEAS
The Ordinary World	Normal World	
Call to Adventure	Inciting Incident	
Refusal of the Call		
Meeting the Mentor		
Crossing the Threshold	Point of No Return	
Tests, Allies & Enemies	Midpoint	
Preparation for the Supreme Ordeal	Midpoint	
The Supreme Ordeal (metamophosis)		
INTERMISSION		
Reward		
The Road Back	The Big Gloom	
The Final Conflict	Climax into Resolution	
Return to Stability	New Normal	

vocal ranges

When creating a breakdown of your musical's characters, be sure to consider their voice types. You can also discuss with your creative team other vocal qualities you want the singer to have (i.e. a warm sound, more operatic, or less refined, etc.). Thinking of this early will help focus your picture of the character and make sure you're writing specifically for a particular voice type.

This chart indicates the standard ranges of each voice type.

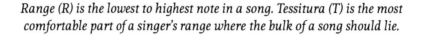

Range (R) is the lowest to highest note in a song. Tessitura (T) is the most comfortable part of a singer's range where the bulk of a song should lie.

Below is a sample of voice ranges in the musical, *A Bronx Tale*.

*For more information on writing for the musical theatre performer's voice, see "**Writing for Today's Musical Theatre Performer**" on MusicalWriters.com.*

MY MUSICAL'S
vocal ranges

Using the staves below, draw in the vocal ranges of each character in your show.
Use this later when creating your character list for auditions.

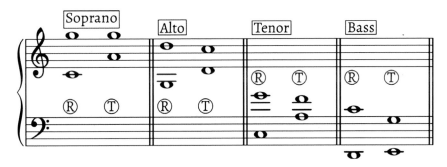

Range (R) is the lowest to highest note in a song. Tessitura (T) is the most comfortable part of a singer's range where the bulk of a song should lie.

Name: _____

Name: _____

Name: _____

Name: _____

Name: _____

Name: _____

Name: _____

Name: _____

Name: _____

MY MUSICAL'S
vocal ranges

Using the staves below, draw in the vocal ranges of each character in your show.
Use this later when creating your character list for auditions.

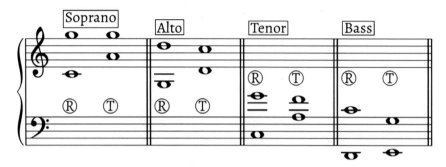

Range (R) is the lowest to highest note in a song. Tessitura (T) is the most comfortable part of a singer's range where the bulk of a song should lie.

Name: _____

Name: _____

Name: _____

Name: _____

Name: _____

Name: _____

Name: _____

Name: _____

Name: _____

MY MUSICAL'S
vocal ranges

Using the staves below, draw in the vocal ranges of each character in your show.
Use this later when creating your character list for auditions.

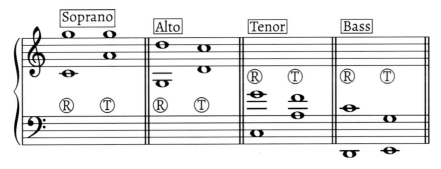

*Range (R) is the lowest to highest note in a song. Tessitura (T) is the most
comfortable part of a singer's range where the bulk of a song should lie.*

Name: _____

Name: _____

Name: _____

Name: _____

Name: _____

Name: _____

Name: _____

Name: _____

Name: _____

rhyme patterns

"Rhyme scheme" or "rhyme pattern" refers to where the rhyming words occur in a verse or a chorus. Use this chart to experiment with rhyming patterns for your songs. You can also use this to diagram your songs and see which rhyming patterns you use most frequently. Do you always use the same pattern? Experiment with some new ones!

1	A
2	B
3	C
4	D

1	A
2	A
3	B
4	C

1	A
2	B
3	B
4	C

1	A
2	B
3	C
4	C

1	A
2	B
3	A
4	C

1	A
2	B
3	C
4	B

1	A
2	B
3	C
4	A

1	A
2	A
3	A
4	B

1	A
2	A
3	B
4	A

1	A
2	B
3	A
4	A

1	A
2	B
3	B
4	B

1	A
2	A
3	A
4	A

1	A
2	A
3	B
4	B

1	A
2	B
3	B
4	A

1	A
2	B
3	A
4	B

chord progressions

Common popular chord progressions follow a pattern that usually (but not always) starts with the tonic chord (which is the I chord) and almost always resolves back to the tonic chord (considered home). Certain chords will tend to create tension while others will lead to a sense of resolution or release of tension. Certain chords will lead to other chords based on the chord tones within the chords and how they relate to the scale derived from the key the song is in.

The image below is a very simple chord progression map for major key progression. This map is very simplistic and does not show all the possibilities.

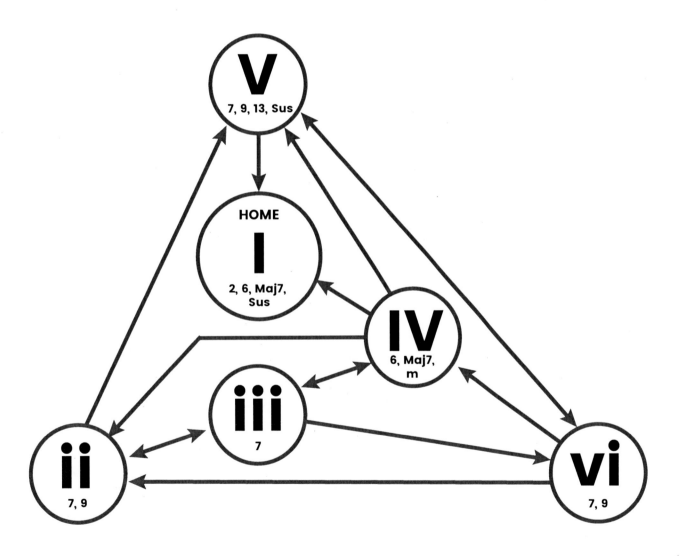

lyric ideas

Song Title: _____ Character: _____

Tempo: _____ Song Type: _____

VERSE

_____

_____

_____

_____

CHORUS

_____

_____

_____

BRIDGE

_____

_____

_____

VERSE

_____

_____

_____

VERSE

_____

_____

_____

BRAINSTORMING
melody ideas

lyric ideas

Song Title: _____   Character: _____

Tempo: _____   Song Type: _____

VERSE

_____

_____

_____

_____

CHORUS

_____

_____

_____

BRIDGE

_____

_____

_____

VERSE

_____

_____

_____

VERSE

_____

_____

_____

BRAINSTORMING
melody ideas

lyric ideas

Song Title: _____   Character: _____

Tempo: _____   Song Type: _____

VERSE

_____
_____
_____
_____

CHORUS

_____
_____
_____

BRIDGE

_____
_____
_____

VERSE

_____
_____
_____

VERSE

_____
_____
_____

lyric ideas

Song Title: _____   Character: _____

Tempo: _____   Song Type: _____

VERSE
_____
_____
_____
_____

CHORUS
_____
_____
_____

BRIDGE
_____
_____
_____

VERSE
_____
_____
_____

VERSE
_____
_____
_____

BRAINSTORMING
melody ideas

lyric ideas

Song Title: _____   Character: _____

Tempo: _____   Song Type: _____

VERSE
_____
_____
_____
_____

CHORUS
_____
_____
_____

BRIDGE
_____
_____
_____

VERSE
_____
_____
_____

VERSE
_____
_____
_____

melody ideas

lyric ideas

Song Title: _____   Character: _____

Tempo: _____   Song Type: _____

VERSE

_____
_____
_____
_____

CHORUS

_____
_____
_____

BRIDGE

_____
_____
_____

VERSE

_____
_____
_____

VERSE

_____
_____
_____

development & readings

development & readings

Once you've written your script and songs, it's time to get it up on its feet so you can see how it works, and if your creative intent translates when it's coming from someone else's mouth.

Every musical's path to production is as unique as its own existence, so there is no one way to get a show produced. If you're willing to put in the effort, there are several steps you can take yourself that will get your show in great shape, help you find supporters and creative team members, give you helpful feedback, and put you in front of the people who can help take you to the next level.

These steps can be done with extravagant budgets as well as on a shoestring*. Let me encourage you to lean towards the latter if you're just starting out. Save your money and your "asks" for when you're further down the road.

If you need help moving through the steps of development, check out our **MusicalWriters Development Series** which provides a coach to guide you through a 12-month development process. Looking for someone to help with demo recordings, arrangements, executive producing, or other technical roles? Check out **MusicalWriters GeniusHub**!

*For tips on keeping your budgets low, see
"How to Self Produce on a Shoestring Budget" at MusicalWriters.com.*

developmental steps

STEP 1   *You've got an **idea**! Check! Step one is done!*

STEP 2   *Check the **rights** on the idea. Is it public domain? Do you need to contact anyone for permission? Find this out and secure rights BEFORE moving forward!*

STEP 3   *Find suitable **collaborators**.*

STEP 4   *Use the 7 Plot Points and the Hero's Journey to **outline the story**. Flesh out three-dimensional **characters**.*

STEP 5   *Create a **first draft** of the script. Then work with your collaborators to **song spot**, and **develop songs** for the important emotional moments of the show.*

STEP 6   *Hold a **Table Reading** to hear the work out loud. **Rewrite** after **feedback**.*

STEP 7   *Get a written **Script Review** by a professional dramaturg or director. Listen, consider, and rewrite.*

STEP 8   *Hold an informal **Staged Reading** or **Concert Reading** of the show to get further feedback as well as build a following of supporters. Rewrite after feedback.*

STEP 9   *Put together a **Pitch Packet** including demo recordings, synopsis, development history. and author bios. Submit to contests and theaters seeking new work.*

STEP 10   *Hold a **29-hour reading** with professional actors, directors, and musicians.*

STEP 11   *Hold a **Workshop Production** and invite artistic directors, producers, and investors.*

STEP 12   *Either self-produce or have your show optioned for a production and enjoy **Opening Night** of your show!*

DEVELOPMENT
steps & tasks

TABLE READING

- [ ] Date / Time / Location
- [ ] Casting
- [ ] Integrated Script & Score
- [ ] Demos & Backing Tracks
- [ ] Seating / Snacks / Drinks
- [ ] Feedback

CONCERT READING

- [ ] Date / Time / Venue
- [ ] Auditions & Casting
- [ ] Modified Script & Score
- [ ] Demos & Rehearsal Tracks
- [ ] Music Director
- [ ] Band or Performance Tracks
- [ ] Invitations / Advertising
- [ ] Sound & Lighting
- [ ] Printed Programs

STAGED READING

- [ ] Date / Time / Venue
- [ ] Casting
- [ ] Integrated Script & Score
- [ ] Demos & Rehearsal Tracks
- [ ] Director & Music Director
- [ ] Rehearsal Space
- [ ] Rehearsal Schedule
- [ ] Band or Performance Tracks
- [ ] Invitations & Advertising
- [ ] Sound & Lighting
- [ ] Printed Programs
- [ ] Audience Feedback

PITCHING

- [ ] One Page Synopsis
- [ ] Demo Recordings
- [ ] Investor Pitch Packet

MARKETING

- [ ] Show Art
- [ ] Website
- [ ] Social Media
- [ ] Paid Advertising
- [ ] Merch

SELF-PRODUCTION

- [ ] Dates / Times / Venue
- [ ] Auditions & Casting
- [ ] Integrated Script & Score
- [ ] Demos & Rehearsal Tracks
- [ ] Director, MD, GM, Stage Manager
- [ ] Rehearsal Space & Schedule
- [ ] Band or Performance Tracks
- [ ] Invitations & Advertising
- [ ] Printed Programs
- [ ] Audience Feedback

table reading

DATE:

TASK	DUE DATE	☑
Set a date, time and place to hold the reading. Be sure there are restrooms and enough chairs available.		
Cast the show using friends and colleagues, and invite them to participate. Be sure to cast someone with the responsibility of reading stage directions.		
Make copies of the script for all participants and distribute early if possible.		
Purchase snacks and drinks.		
Send a reminder email or text asking participants to confirm.		
If possible, highlight all scripts according to character/actor role and write the actor's or actress's name on the front. Provide binders if possible.		
Set up table, chairs, refreshments, pencils, highlighters and printed scripts.		
At the reading, briefly introduce the project and explain that this reading is for the purpose of hearing the work "out loud" and for feedback.		
Invite all attending to make notes or highlight areas to discuss following the reading.		
Use your phone to record the reading so you can listen again later.		
Read the work! Just read the lyrics, no music needed. Break for snacks and restroom at intermission or halfway through if it is one act.		
When finished, ask for feedback from all. Be respectful and not defensive about the work. Thank everyone for their participation.		
Send a hand-written thank-you note to all who participated in the reading. Expressed gratefulness always pays off.		

NOTES:

DATE:

TASK	DUE DATE	
Determine your priorities, budget and desired outcomes for the reading. Look at the included worksheet "Budget Planning: Staged Reading" to help plan costs.		
Set a date, time and place to hold the reading. A facility with a stage is fine but not absolutely necessary. If renting a facility, secure the space with a deposit or payment.		
Cast the show through auditions, personal selections, or a casting director. Be sure to cast someone with the responsibility of reading stage directions.		
Make copies of the script and score, place in binders, and distribute to cast at least 6 weeks before the reading. Integrate the score into the script if possible.		
Secure a director and music director if needed. Provide script and score as soon as possible. Determine musicians and instruments needed, book them, and send score.		
If you are doing any fundraising, create a pitch packet and schedule meetings with potential donors/investors. Also consider selling program ads to offset costs.		
If not being handled by the director, schedule individual, private rehearsals with singers to learn music. Also schedule group rehearsals for ensemble songs.		
Send invitations and announcements to the public or invitees.		
Schedule walk-through rehearsal with entire cast. Inform cast on performance call times and appropriate dress.		
If you are directing, be sure to consider which music stand each performer will go to for each scene. Mark the music stands and walk through this with performers.		
Create a printed program including participant names, bios, order of songs, and a synopsis of the show. Also include a way for the audience to respond with feedback.		
Set up the room for the reading. Have enough chairs and music stands for all and be sure chairs and stands are marked appropriately.		
Enjoy a wonderful performance of your show! You did it!		
Send a hand-written thank-you note with stipend/gift to all who participated in the reading. Also send thank-you email to audience members if possible.		

concert reading

DATE:

TASK	DUE DATE	
Determine your priorities, budget and desired outcomes for the reading. Look at the included worksheet "Budget Planning: Staged Reading" to help plan costs.		
Set a date, time and place to hold the reading. A facility with a stage is fine but not absolutely necessary. If renting a facility, secure the space with a deposit or payment.		
Cast the show through auditions or personal selections. It's also helpful to cast someone as a narrator to read explanatory lead-ins to each musical number.		
Place copies of the score in binders and distribute to performers at least 6 weeks early. If you are including dialogue within songs, integrate that into the score.		
Secure a music director if needed. Determine musicians and instruments needed, book them, and send score.		
If you are doing any fundraising, create a pitch packet and schedule meetings with potential donors/investors. Also consider selling program ads to offset costs.		
If not being handled by the director, schedule individual, private rehearsals with singers to learn music. Also schedule group rehearsals for ensemble songs.		
Send invitations and announcements to the public or invitees.		
Schedule walk-through rehearsal with entire cast. Inform cast on performance call times and appropriate dress.		
If you are directing, be sure to consider which music stand each performer will go to for each number. Mark the music stands and walk through this with performers.		
Create a printed program including participant names, bios, order of songs, and a synopsis of the show. Also include a way for the audience to respond with feedback.		
Set up the room for the reading. Have enough chairs and music stands for all and be sure chairs and stands are marked appropriately.		
Enjoy a wonderful performance of your show! You did it!		
Send a hand-written thank-you note with stipend/gift to all who participated in the reading. Also send thank-you email to audience members if possible.		

READING PARTICIPANT
contact information

	NAME	CHARACTER/ROLE	EMAIL / PHONE / MAILING ADDRESS	CONFIRMED
1.				
2.				
3.				
4.				
5.				
6.				
7.				
8.				
9.				
10.				
11.				
12.				

*Be sure to send a reminder a few days prior to the reading and
request a confirmation from each participant.*

READING PARTICIPANT
contact information

NAME	CHARACTER/ROLE	EMAIL / PHONE / MAILING ADDRESS	CONFIRMED
1.			
2.			
3.			
4.			
5.			
6.			
7.			
8.			
9.			
10.			
11.			
12.			

Be sure to send a reminder a few days prior to the reading and
request a confirmation from each participant.

STAGED READING
budget planner

	Qty		$ each	Estimate	Actual
FEES/SALARIES					
Actor Stipend		x		$	$
Musicians		x		$	$
Audition Accompanist				$	$
Director				$	$
Musical Director				$	$
Stage Manager				$	$
Press Agent				$	$
General Manager				$	$
Audio/Video Recording				$	$
Casting Director				$	$
				$	$
				$	$
PHYSICAL PRODUCTION/RENTALS					
Audio Rental (mics/sound)				$	$
Lighting Rental				$	$
Music Stands				$	$
Props				$	$
				$	$
				$	$
GENERAL & ADMINISTRATIVE					
Performance Space				$	$
Rehearsal Space				$	$
Custodial Service				$	$
Script/Music Printing/Binding		x		$	$
Marketing/Advertising				$	$
Program Design				$	$
Program Printing				$	$
Refreshments				$	$
Transportation				$	$
Insurance				$	$
Legal Fees				$	$
Contingency / Misc				$	$
				$	$
				$	$
TOTAL ESTIMATED COSTS				$	
TOTAL ACTUAL COSTS					$
Income					$
Recoup					$

budget planner

	Qty		$ each	Estimate	Actual
FEES/SALARIES					
Actor Stipend		x		$	$
Musicians		x		$	$
Audition Accompanist				$	$
Director				$	$
Musical Director				$	$
Stage Manager				$	$
Press Agent				$	$
General Manager				$	$
Audio/Video Recording				$	$
Casting Director				$	$
				$	$
				$	$
PHYSICAL PRODUCTION/RENTALS					
Audio Rental (mics/sound)				$	$
Lighting Rental				$	$
Music Stands				$	$
Props				$	$
				$	$
				$	$
GENERAL & ADMINISTRATIVE					
Performance Space				$	$
Rehearsal Space				$	$
Custodial Service				$	$
Script/Music Printing/Binding		x		$	$
Marketing/Advertising				$	$
Program Design				$	$
Program Printing				$	$
Refreshments				$	$
Transportation				$	$
Insurance				$	$
Legal Fees				$	$
Contingency / Misc				$	$
				$	$
				$	$
TOTAL ESTIMATED COSTS				$	
TOTAL ACTUAL COSTS					$
Income					$
Recoup					$

priority matrix

No matter how engaged, invested, and detail-oriented you may be, it's impossible to execute every task with the same level of attention—it's also not necessary. By choosing activities intelligently, we can avoid time-depleting projects that stop us moving forward. Consider all the tasks for your upcoming project and try to organize them into the appropriate category. Then execute accordingly.

PROJECT:

URGENT **NOT URGENT**

NOT IMPORTANT

Urgent but Not Important
(batch or outsource)

1. _____
2. _____
3. _____
4. _____
5. _____

Not Urgent and Not Important
(optional or long-term projects)

1. _____
2. _____
3. _____
4. _____
5. _____

IMPORTANT

Urgent and Important
(first on the to-do list)

1. _____
2. _____
3. _____
4. _____
5. _____

Not Urgent but Important
(prioritize with time blocking)

1. _____
2. _____
3. _____
4. _____
5. _____

priority matrix

PROJECT: _____

	URGENT	NOT URGENT

URGENT   NOT URGENT

NOT IMPORTANT

Urgent but Not Important
(batch or outsource)

1. _____
2. _____
3. _____
4. _____
5. _____

Not Urgent and Not Important
(optional or long-term projects)

1. _____
2. _____
3. _____
4. _____
5. _____

IMPORTANT

Urgent and Important
(first on the to-do list)

1. _____
2. _____
3. _____
4. _____
5. _____

Not Urgent but Important
(prioritize with time blocking)

1. _____
2. _____
3. _____
4. _____
5. _____

rehearsal call list

Saturday, May 4	Theater Three • Stage 2	CALLED
12:00-1:00PM	Music with John	Smith, Johnson, Baez
1:00-2:00PM	Scene work with Sarah	Walden, Cox
Notes		

SAMPLE
rehearsal schedule

Date	Time	Scene(s)	Venue	Cast Required	Notes
3/4	8-9 am	1, 4, 5	Studio 214b	Smith, Cox	choreo

EVENT: _____

rehearsal call list

EVENT: _____

rehearsal schedule

Date	Time	Scene(s)	Venue	Cast Required	Notes

SECTION SEVEN

submissions
& marketing

submissions & marketing

Once your musical is in good shape (read: had a couple script reviews, a few readings, and many rounds of rewrites), then it's time to launch it into the world.

There are many theaters, producers, and organizations who are open to new work*, and being selected into their programs can do wonders for your show (and your confidence). Before you submit, read the guidelines for submission (they're all different), and be sure your script is formatted according to industry standards.

It's also good to start working on your marketing materials so you can start to build brand awareness. **Branding** is the process of giving meaning to your show by creating and shaping a specific image, impression, or emotion in consumers' minds. Jeff Bezos, founder and CEO of Amazon, says, "Branding is what people say about you when you're not in the room." It's what differentiates you from others in the market.

Now that you have a full musical, it's time to start thinking about it as a product, and you're the CEO in charge of moving it forward. Who is your audience, and how will you reach them? That's marketing.

*For a calendar and list of over 80 musical submission opportunities, check out our **Academy Membership** at MusicalWriters.com.

CREATING YOUR MUSICAL'S
submissions packet

Submissions applications are all different. A few are open-ended ("Send your materials to ....") but most are very specific about what and how they want your musical information sent. Here are several documents they could ask for, so go ahead and have these prepared and create a copy in PDF format.

☐ Cover letter with a personal greeting

☐ Links to demos on your Dropbox, website, Soundcloud, or other online platform

☐ Cast/Character Breakdown
- Include gender, age, race, vocal range, and brief description of character and personality
- For vocal range, specify either voice part (such as tenor or mezzo) or give highest and lowest notes sung by the character across all songs
- Indicate possible or necessary doubling

☐ One page synopsis

☐ 10-page script sample

☐ Full script, formatted to industry standards

☐ Blind script (no contact information on the script), formatted to industry standards

☐ Lyrics sheets of demo songs

☐ Score/Notated Form of each song

☐ Writer bios

☐ Production/Development History

☐ Audience Appeal (Why this show? Why now?)

☐ Playwright's Resume

☐ Artistic Statement

☐ Proof of secured rights/permissions (if applicable)

☐ Contact information

marketing map

The further you go down the road of development, the more attention and publicity your show will naturally receive. At some point, all of these pieces will come into play.

Use the blank boxes in the below diagram to make notes on contacts, deadline, related events, and ideas for these various promotional channels.

DEMOS/VIDEO

PRESS RELEASE

MERCH

SOCIAL MEDIA ——— MY SHOW ——— WEBSITE

PROMO ITEMS

MAILING LIST

SHOW ART

website outline

These are the basic pages you'll need on your show website.
Fill in the blanks with what you want on each page. This can serve
as both an outline for your web designer as well as a checklist for the items
you need to provide them for each web page.

For the **Story** page, you can either include a full synopsis of the show or a simple overview, similar to your elevator pitch. You can also share the theme or origination story if applicable.

- ☐ Full Synopsis
- ☐ Overview/Pitch
- ☐ _____
- ☐ _____

Your **Music** page should include either embedded mp3s or and embedded SoundCloud playlist. Try not to link to external sites if possible so your reader stays on your main site.

- ☐ Embedded MP3 demos
- ☐ Embedded SoundCloud
- ☐ _____
- ☐ _____

Depending on where you are in development, the **Creative Team** page can contain bios of just the writers (book, lyrics, music) or other associated members such as directors, producers, etc.

- ☐ Bookwriter Bio
- ☐ Lyricist Bio
- ☐ Composer Bio
- ☐ _____

STORY　　　　**MUSIC**　　　　**CREATIVE TEAM**

Home Page

DEVELOPMENT HISTORY　　　　**CONTACT**　　　　**OTHER**

On the **Development History** page, you can list all previous performances or readings with theaters, locations and dates. You could also include a blog where you write articles on each event.

- ☐ List of Readings
- ☐ Theaters/Locations/Dates
- ☐ Blog Articles
- ☐ News & Media Mentions

Instead of putting your email address on your website, it's often better to include a **Contact** page. This page can house a form which will filter and reduce spam. Include these input areas:

- ☐ Contact Name (first & last)
- ☐ Contact Email Address
- ☐ Contact Phone
- ☐ Message

If you have great photos, you can create a gallery page to share so they don't overwhelm the other pages on the site. You can also have pages for merchandise, ticket sales, upcoming performances, etc.

- ☐ Photo Gallery
- ☐ _____
- ☐ _____
- ☐ _____

*Need someone to create your website or show art? Our team at **Reed Creative Group** is ready to help.*
*Email Holly at **hollyr@reedcreativegroup.com** and let's chat!*

SECTION EIGHT

setting goals

setting goals

Zig Ziglar said, "If you aim at nothing, you'll hit it every time."

Nothing is more frustrating than waiting on someone else to accomplish your vision. It's YOUR show, so you're responsible. Take the reins!

The next pages were designed to help you set the outcome for your goals and create steps and a deadline for making them happen. Be sure you're setting SMART goals (see below).

Consider how you'll keep yourself accountable to your goals. The best way is to involve other people, ideally your collaborators. When you all have skin in the game, the incentive is solid.

It's also important to establish some rewards along the way. Whether it's dinner at a fancy restaurant, a splurge for new tech, or anything else that suits your fancy, give yourself permission to enjoy the results of your hard work!

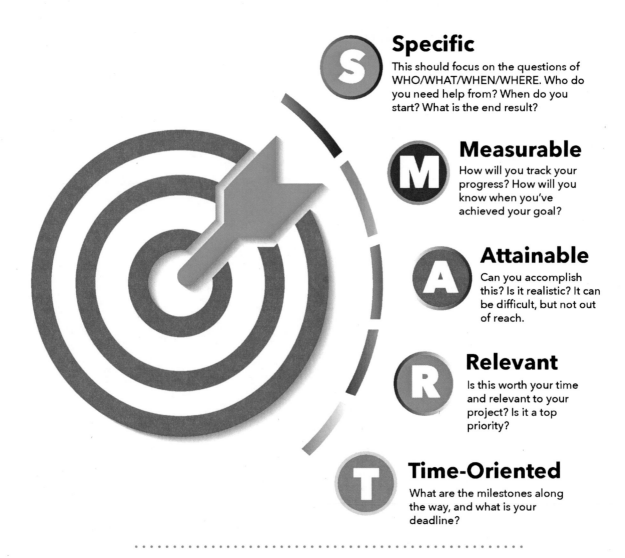

S Specific
This should focus on the questions of WHO/WHAT/WHEN/WHERE. Who do you need help from? When do you start? What is the end result?

M Measurable
How will you track your progress? How will you know when you've achieved your goal?

A Attainable
Can you accomplish this? Is it realistic? It can be difficult, but not out of reach.

R Relevant
Is this worth your time and relevant to your project? Is it a top priority?

T Time-Oriented
What are the milestones along the way, and what is your deadline?

year one goals

Year: _____

Quarter 1 Focus:

JAN	☐ _____ ☐ _____ ☐ _____
FEB	☐ _____ ☐ _____ ☐ _____
MARCH	☐ _____ ☐ _____ ☐ _____

Quarter 2 Focus:

APRIL	☐ _____ ☐ _____ ☐ _____
MAY	☐ _____ ☐ _____ ☐ _____
JUNE	☐ _____ ☐ _____ ☐ _____

Quarter 3 Focus:

JULY	☐ _____ ☐ _____ ☐ _____
AUG	☐ _____ ☐ _____ ☐ _____
SEPT	☐ _____ ☐ _____ ☐ _____

Quarter 4 Focus:

OCT	☐ _____ ☐ _____ ☐ _____
NOV	☐ _____ ☐ _____ ☐ _____
DEC	☐ _____ ☐ _____ ☐ _____

year two goals

Year: _____

Quarter 1 Focus:

JAN	☐ _____
	☐ _____
	☐ _____
FEB	☐ _____
	☐ _____
	☐ _____
MARCH	☐ _____
	☐ _____
	☐ _____

Quarter 2 Focus:

APRIL	☐ _____
	☐ _____
	☐ _____
MAY	☐ _____
	☐ _____
	☐ _____
JUNE	☐ _____
	☐ _____
	☐ _____

Quarter 3 Focus:

JULY	☐ _____
	☐ _____
	☐ _____
AUG	☐ _____
	☐ _____
	☐ _____
SEPT	☐ _____
	☐ _____
	☐ _____

Quarter 4 Focus:

OCT	☐ _____
	☐ _____
	☐ _____
NOV	☐ _____
	☐ _____
	☐ _____
DEC	☐ _____
	☐ _____
	☐ _____

year three goals

Year: _____

Quarter 1 Focus:

JAN	☐ _____ ☐ _____ ☐ _____
FEB	☐ _____ ☐ _____ ☐ _____
MARCH	☐ _____ ☐ _____ ☐ _____

Quarter 2 Focus:

APRIL	☐ _____ ☐ _____ ☐ _____
MAY	☐ _____ ☐ _____ ☐ _____
JUNE	☐ _____ ☐ _____ ☐ _____

Quarter 3 Focus:

JULY	☐ _____ ☐ _____ ☐ _____
AUG	☐ _____ ☐ _____ ☐ _____
SEPT	☐ _____ ☐ _____ ☐ _____

Quarter 4 Focus:

OCT	☐ _____ ☐ _____ ☐ _____
NOV	☐ _____ ☐ _____ ☐ _____
DEC	☐ _____ ☐ _____ ☐ _____

year four goals

Year: _____

Quarter 1 Focus:

JAN	☐ _____
	☐ _____
	☐ _____
FEB	☐ _____
	☐ _____
	☐ _____
MARCH	☐ _____
	☐ _____
	☐ _____

Quarter 2 Focus:

APRIL	☐ _____
	☐ _____
	☐ _____
MAY	☐ _____
	☐ _____
	☐ _____
JUNE	☐ _____
	☐ _____
	☐ _____

Quarter 3 Focus:

JULY	☐ _____
	☐ _____
	☐ _____
AUG	☐ _____
	☐ _____
	☐ _____
SEPT	☐ _____
	☐ _____
	☐ _____

Quarter 4 Focus:

OCT	☐ _____
	☐ _____
	☐ _____
NOV	☐ _____
	☐ _____
	☐ _____
DEC	☐ _____
	☐ _____
	☐ _____

year five goals

Year: _____

Quarter 1 Focus:

JAN	☐ _____ ☐ _____ ☐ _____
FEB	☐ _____ ☐ _____ ☐ _____
MARCH	☐ _____ ☐ _____ ☐ _____

Quarter 2 Focus:

APRIL	☐ _____ ☐ _____ ☐ _____
MAY	☐ _____ ☐ _____ ☐ _____
JUNE	☐ _____ ☐ _____ ☐ _____

Quarter 3 Focus:

JULY	☐ _____ ☐ _____ ☐ _____
AUG	☐ _____ ☐ _____ ☐ _____
SEPT	☐ _____ ☐ _____ ☐ _____

Quarter 4 Focus:

OCT	☐ _____ ☐ _____ ☐ _____
NOV	☐ _____ ☐ _____ ☐ _____
DEC	☐ _____ ☐ _____ ☐ _____

goal planner

☐ Bookwriting ☐ Lyrics ☐ Music ☐ Development ☐ Marketing Deadline: _____

Define your goal: _____

_____

Why is this important to you? _____

_____

What's your plan? _____

_____

_____

_____

MILESTONE #1

☐ _____

_____

MILESTONE #1 TASKS:

_____
_____
_____
_____
_____
_____
_____
_____
_____
_____

MILESTONE #2

☐ _____

_____

MILESTONE #2 TASKS:

_____
_____
_____
_____
_____
_____
_____
_____
_____
_____

MILESTONE #3

☐ _____

_____

MILESTONE #3 TASKS:

_____
_____
_____
_____
_____
_____
_____
_____
_____
_____

REWARD: _____

goal planner

☐ Bookwriting   ☐ Lyrics   ☐ Music   ☐ Development   ☐ Marketing   Deadline: _____

Define your goal: _____

_____

Why is this important to you? _____

_____

What's your plan? _____

_____

_____

_____

MILESTONE #1

☐ _____

_____

MILESTONE #1 TASKS:

_____
_____
_____
_____
_____
_____
_____
_____
_____
_____
_____

MILESTONE #2

☐ _____

_____

MILESTONE #2 TASKS:

_____
_____
_____
_____
_____
_____
_____
_____
_____
_____
_____

MILESTONE #3

☐ _____

_____

MILESTONE #3 TASKS:

_____
_____
_____
_____
_____
_____
_____
_____
_____
_____
_____

REWARD: _____

goal planner

☐ Bookwriting   ☐ Lyrics   ☐ Music   ☐ Development   ☐ Marketing   Deadline: _____

Define your goal: _____

_____

Why is this important to you? _____

_____

What's your plan? _____

_____

_____

_____

MILESTONE #1

☐ _____

_____

MILESTONE #1 TASKS:

_____

_____

_____

_____

_____

_____

_____

_____

_____

_____

_____

MILESTONE #2

☐ _____

_____

MILESTONE #2 TASKS:

_____

_____

_____

_____

_____

_____

_____

_____

_____

_____

_____

MILESTONE #3

☐ _____

_____

MILESTONE #3 TASKS:

_____

_____

_____

_____

_____

_____

_____

_____

_____

_____

_____

REWARD: _____

goal planner

☐ Bookwriting ☐ Lyrics ☐ Music ☐ Development ☐ Marketing   Deadline: _____

Define your goal: _____

_____

Why is this important to you? _____

_____

What's your plan? _____

_____

_____

_____

MILESTONE #1

☐ _____

_____

MILESTONE #1 TASKS:

_____
_____
_____
_____
_____
_____
_____
_____
_____
_____

MILESTONE #2

☐ _____

_____

MILESTONE #2 TASKS:

_____
_____
_____
_____
_____
_____
_____
_____
_____
_____

MILESTONE #3

☐ _____

_____

MILESTONE #3 TASKS:

_____
_____
_____
_____
_____
_____
_____
_____
_____
_____

REWARD: _____

to do lists

CATEGORY:

- [ ]
- [ ]
- [ ]
- [ ]
- [ ]
- [ ]
- [ ]

CATEGORY:

- [ ]
- [ ]
- [ ]
- [ ]
- [ ]
- [ ]
- [ ]

CATEGORY:

- [ ]
- [ ]
- [ ]
- [ ]
- [ ]
- [ ]
- [ ]

CATEGORY:

- [ ]
- [ ]
- [ ]
- [ ]
- [ ]
- [ ]
- [ ]

to do lists

CATEGORY:

- [ ]
- [ ]
- [ ]
- [ ]
- [ ]
- [ ]
- [ ]

CATEGORY:

- [ ]
- [ ]
- [ ]
- [ ]
- [ ]
- [ ]
- [ ]

CATEGORY:

- [ ]
- [ ]
- [ ]
- [ ]
- [ ]
- [ ]
- [ ]

CATEGORY:

- [ ]
- [ ]
- [ ]
- [ ]
- [ ]
- [ ]
- [ ]

event planner

EVENT DESCRIPTION

TO DO LIST

1. _____ ☐

2. _____ ☐

3. _____ ☐

4. _____ ☐

5. _____ ☐

6. _____ ☐

7. _____ ☐

8. _____ ☐

9. _____ ☐

10. _____ ☐

DATE	MILESTONE
__/__/__	
__/__/__	
__/__/__	
__/__/__	
__/__/__	
__/__/__	
__/__/__	
__/__/__	
__/__/__	
__/__/__	

NOTES

event planner

EVENT DESCRIPTION

TO DO LIST

1. _____ ☐

2. _____ ☐

3. _____ ☐

4. _____ ☐

5. _____ ☐

6. _____ ☐

7. _____ ☐

8. _____ ☐

9. _____ ☐

10. _____ ☐

DATE   MILESTONE

/   /   _____

/   /   _____

/   /   _____

/   /   _____

/   /   _____

/   /   _____

/   /   _____

/   /   _____

/   /   _____

/   /   _____

NOTES

event planner

EVENT DESCRIPTION

TO DO LIST

1. _____ ☐

2. _____ ☐

3. _____ ☐

4. _____ ☐

5. _____ ☐

6. _____ ☐

DATE   MILESTONE

7. _____ ☐

/ /   [ ]

8. _____ ☐

/ /   [ ]

9. _____ ☐

/ /   [ ]

/ /   [ ]

10. _____ ☐

/ /   [ ]

/ /   [ ]

NOTES

/ /   [ ]

/ /   [ ]

/ /   [ ]

/ /   [ ]

event planner

EVENT DESCRIPTION

TO DO LIST

1. _____ ☐

2. _____ ☐

3. _____ ☐

4. _____ ☐

5. _____ ☐

6. _____ ☐

7. _____ ☐

8. _____ ☐

9. _____ ☐

10. _____ ☐

DATE   MILESTONE

/ /	
/ /	
/ /	
/ /	
/ /	
/ /	
/ /	
/ /	
/ /	
/ /	

NOTES

event planner

EVENT DESCRIPTION

TO DO LIST

1. _____ ☐

2. _____ ☐

3. _____ ☐

4. _____ ☐

5. _____ ☐

6. _____ ☐

7. _____ ☐

8. _____ ☐

9. _____ ☐

10. _____ ☐

DATE   ### MILESTONE

/ / [   ]

/ / [   ]

/ / [   ]

/ / [   ]

/ / [   ]

/ / [   ]

/ / [   ]

/ / [   ]

/ / [   ]

/ / [   ]

NOTES

SECTION NINE

monthly planner

· ·

TO DO & NOTES	SUNDAY	MONDAY	TUESDAY

GOAL:

WEDNESDAY	THURSDAY	FRIDAY	SATURDAY

MONTH:

TO DO & NOTES	SUNDAY	MONDAY	TUESDAY

WEDNESDAY	THURSDAY	FRIDAY	SATURDAY

MONTH:

TO DO & NOTES	SUNDAY	MONDAY	TUESDAY

WEDNESDAY	THURSDAY	FRIDAY	SATURDAY

MONTH:

TO DO & NOTES	SUNDAY	MONDAY	TUESDAY

GOAL:

WEDNESDAY	THURSDAY	FRIDAY	SATURDAY

MONTH:

TO DO & NOTES	SUNDAY	MONDAY	TUESDAY

GOAL:

WEDNESDAY	THURSDAY	FRIDAY	SATURDAY

TO DO & NOTES	SUNDAY	MONDAY	TUESDAY

WEDNESDAY	THURSDAY	FRIDAY	SATURDAY

MONTH:

TO DO & NOTES	SUNDAY	MONDAY	TUESDAY

GOAL:

WEDNESDAY	THURSDAY	FRIDAY	SATURDAY

TO DO & NOTES	SUNDAY	MONDAY	TUESDAY

WEDNESDAY	THURSDAY	FRIDAY	SATURDAY

MONTH:

TO DO & NOTES	SUNDAY	MONDAY	TUESDAY

WEDNESDAY	THURSDAY	FRIDAY	SATURDAY

TO DO & NOTES	SUNDAY	MONDAY	TUESDAY

WEDNESDAY	THURSDAY	FRIDAY	SATURDAY

TO DO & NOTES	SUNDAY	MONDAY	TUESDAY

WEDNESDAY	THURSDAY	FRIDAY	SATURDAY

TO DO & NOTES	SUNDAY	MONDAY	TUESDAY

GOAL:

WEDNESDAY	THURSDAY	FRIDAY	SATURDAY

contacts & important info

contact list

| NAME | EMAIL |
| TITLE/ COMPANY | PHONE |

| NAME | EMAIL |
| TITLE/ COMPANY | PHONE |

| NAME | EMAIL |
| TITLE/ COMPANY | PHONE |

| NAME | EMAIL |
| TITLE/ COMPANY | PHONE |

| NAME | EMAIL |
| TITLE/ COMPANY | PHONE |

| NAME | EMAIL |
| TITLE/ COMPANY | PHONE |

| NAME | EMAIL |
| TITLE/ COMPANY | PHONE |

| NAME | EMAIL |
| TITLE/ COMPANY | PHONE |

| NAME | EMAIL |
| TITLE/ COMPANY | PHONE |

| NAME | EMAIL |
| TITLE/ COMPANY | PHONE |

contact list

NAME

TITLE/
COMPANY

EMAIL

PHONE

NAME

TITLE/
COMPANY

EMAIL

PHONE

NAME

TITLE/
COMPANY

EMAIL

PHONE

NAME

TITLE/
COMPANY

EMAIL

PHONE

NAME

TITLE/
COMPANY

EMAIL

PHONE

NAME

TITLE/
COMPANY

EMAIL

PHONE

NAME

TITLE/
COMPANY

EMAIL

PHONE

NAME

TITLE/
COMPANY

EMAIL

PHONE

NAME

TITLE/
COMPANY

EMAIL

PHONE

NAME

TITLE/
COMPANY

EMAIL

PHONE

IMPORTANT
conversations

CONVERSATION WITH: _____ DATE: _____

☐ Bookwriting ☐ Lyrics ☐ Music ☐ Development ☐ Marketing

NOTES:

_____

_____

_____

_____

_____

_____

_____

_____

_____

_____

_____

_____

_____

_____

_____

_____

_____

_____

_____

_____

_____

IMPORTANT
conversations

CONVERSATION WITH: _____   DATE: _____

☐ Bookwriting   ☐ Lyrics   ☐ Music   ☐ Development   ☐ Marketing

NOTES:

_____

_____

_____

_____

_____

_____

_____

_____

_____

_____

_____

_____

_____

_____

_____

_____

_____

_____

_____

IMPORTANT
conversations

CONVERSATION WITH: _____   DATE: _____

☐ Bookwriting   ☐ Lyrics   ☐ Music   ☐ Development   ☐ Marketing

NOTES:

_____

_____

_____

_____

_____

_____

_____

_____

_____

_____

_____

_____

_____

_____

_____

_____

_____

_____

IMPORTANT
conversations

CONVERSATION WITH: _____ DATE: _____

☐ Bookwriting ☐ Lyrics ☐ Music ☐ Development ☐ Marketing

NOTES:

_____

_____

_____

_____

_____

_____

_____

_____

_____

_____

_____

_____

_____

_____

_____

_____

_____

_____

IMPORTANT
conversations

CONVERSATION WITH: _____   DATE: _____

☐ Bookwriting   ☐ Lyrics   ☐ Music   ☐ Development   ☐ Marketing

NOTES:

_____

_____

_____

_____

_____

_____

_____

_____

_____

_____

_____

_____

_____

_____

_____

_____

_____

_____

IMPORTANT
conversations

CONVERSATION WITH: _____ DATE: _____

☐ Bookwriting   ☐ Lyrics   ☐ Music   ☐ Development   ☐ Marketing

NOTES:

_____

_____

_____

_____

_____

_____

_____

_____

_____

_____

_____

_____

_____

_____

_____

_____

_____

CONVERSATION WITH: _____ **DATE:** _____

☐ Bookwriting   ☐ Lyrics   ☐ Music   ☐ Development   ☐ Marketing

NOTES:

_____

_____

_____

_____

_____

_____

_____

_____

_____

_____

_____

_____

_____

_____

_____

_____

_____

_____

_____

IMPORTANT
conversations

CONVERSATION WITH: _____   DATE: _____

☐ Bookwriting   ☐ Lyrics   ☐ Music   ☐ Development   ☐ Marketing

NOTES:

_____

_____

_____

_____

_____

_____

_____

_____

_____

_____

_____

_____

_____

_____

_____

_____

_____

_____

_____

_____

IMPORTANT
conversations

CONVERSATION WITH: _____ DATE: _____

☐ Bookwriting ☐ Lyrics ☐ Music ☐ Development ☐ Marketing

NOTES:

_____

_____

_____

_____

_____

_____

_____

_____

_____

_____

_____

_____

_____

_____

_____

_____

_____

recommended resources

Beating Broadway: How to Create Stories for Musicals That Get Standing Ovations

This interesting guide by Steve Cuden focuses on story construction for musicals, from the inciting incidents to the resolutions. Then Cuden outlines the narrative beats of 40 popular musicals, laying out how their storytelling works.

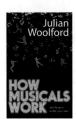

How Musicals Work: And How To Write Your Own

Julian Woolford is a long-time director, teacher, and writer in the UK. His book is easy to follow and provides a solid foundation for the musical writing craft. For his points about story structure, he draws from the work of Joseph Campbell (The Hero with a Thousand Faces) and Christopher Vogler (The Writer's Journey), showing how the hero of the story makes a journey that ultimately inspires the audience. Woolford also covers song spotting, development of characters, lyrics, music, and more.

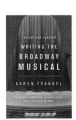

Writing the Broadway Musical

Aaron Frankel's book is almost more of a reference source than a "how-to" guide. It has a rather dense academic style, but he does offer insights and examples that may be useful to lyricists and other readers.

The Musical Theatre Writer's Survival Guide

David Spencer has been a critic as well as a musical writer, and he shares his opinions along with craft notes in this interesting book. He has been on the faculty of the BMI-Lehman Engel Musical Theatre Workshop. As an experienced teacher, he wisely shares examples illustrating his points when he examines book, music, and lyrics. He also covers some of the practical aspects of musical making.

Making Musicals: An Informal Introduction to the World of Musical Theatre

Tom Jones is best known for being the lyricist/librettist of *The Fantasticks*. He draws from his theatrical experiences for Making Musicals, and in this short book, he shares stories related to the components of the musical art form.

Writing Musical Theater

Allen Cohen and Steven L. Rosenhaus are experienced composers who teach musical theater writing at the college level. Their book includes foundational material but also ventures into some advanced music and lyrics commentary. It provides craft details and examples that could be especially helpful for experienced writers, although novice writers report finding it valuable as well.

suggested reading

The Secret Life of the American Musical

Structured like a musical, The Secret Life of the American Musical begins with an overture and concludes with a curtain call, with stops in between for "I Want" songs, "conditional" love songs, production numbers, star turns, and finales. Jack Viertel shows us patterns in the architecture of classic shows and charts the inevitable evolution that has taken place in musical theater as America itself has evolved socially and politically.

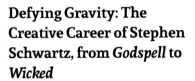

Defying Gravity: The Creative Career of Stephen Schwartz, from *Godspell* to *Wicked*

Carol de Giere covers not only the making of Schwartz musicals, but the advice and "Creativity Notes" from this successful musical writer who has guided other musical writers for over three decades through the ASCAP Musical Theatre Workshops.

Story: Substance, Structure, Style and the Principles of Screenwriting

Robert McKee's Story is one of the classic texts for screenwriters. McKee explores how story structure works to inspire an audience, based on some of Aristotle's principles and his own analysis. Note especially his comments on layers of conflict, the gap between expectation and results, and cast design.

Save the Cat

This popular book for screenwriting is one of the rare sources for details about creating a storyboard with index cards (Final Draft software has an electronic version of this). Many musical writers use storyboards for working out the structure of a show. Save The Cat is a good place to learn the process.

OUR FAVORITE
software tools

Finale

Produce the music of your imagination without compromise with Finale notation software. At every rehearsal, know that your score will sound great, your parts are ready, and you have clearly communicated your musical vision.

www.finalemusic.com/free-trial

Final Draft

Final Draft software is the scriptwriting standard of the entertainment industry, combining powerful word processing with professional script formatting so you can focus more on character and story.

www.musicalwriters.com/tryfinaldraft

GarageBand

GarageBand is a fully equipped music creation studio right inside your Mac — with a complete sound library that includes instruments, presets for guitar and voice, and an incredible selection of session drummers and percussionists.

www.apple.com/mac/garageband

RhymeZone

RhymeZone is a completely free online rhyming dictionary. It's simple, powerful, and comprehensive. They also have a great iPhone app to keep rhymes (and a thesaurus) at your fingertips.

www.rhymezone.com

resources

MUSICALWRITERS.COM

MusicalWriters.com

MusicalWriters.com exists to encourage, educate and equip musical theatre writers. You'll find tips on writing musicals, interviews with Broadway leaders, an extensive list of submission opportunities, helpful online courses, online Writer Groups, and an amazing community of writers.

MusicalWriters GeniusHub

MusicalWriters GeniusHub is your source for music and script services including transcription, music and vocal arranging, digital audio production, editing and formatting, and more. Visit to find or become a Genius!

GENIUSHUB.MUSICALWRITERS.COM

THEATERMAKERSSTUDIO.COM

The TheaterMakers Studio

The TheaterMakers Studio, created by Tony Award-winning producer Ken Davenport, is a digital training program and community for theater makers at all stages in the process who want to get produced and take their career to the next stage.

New Musicals, Inc.

New Musicals Inc., hosts many programs which support new musicals in development. Our academic wing, the Academy for Musical Theatre, offers courses, both online and live in Los Angeles, for professional musical theatre writers.

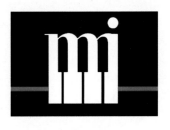

NMI.ORG

resources

The Dramatists Guild

DRAMATISTSGUILD.COM

The Dramatists Guild of America is a professional organization for playwrights, composers, and lyricists working in the U.S. theatre market. Membership as an Associate Member is open to any person having written at least one stage play.

Maestra Music

Maestra Music was founded by composer/lyricist and music director Georgia Stitt to give support, visibility, and community to the women who make the music in the musical theater industry.

MAESTRAMUSIC.ORG

The Commercial Theater Institute

COMMERCIALTHEATERINSTITUTE.COM

CTI is the theatre industry's leading training and professional development program for emerging producers. It covers the widest range of topics and features over 100 of the most distinguished industry professionals as lecturers and panelists.

Theater Resources Unlimited

Theater Resources Unlimited (TRU) is a nonprofit organization created to help producers produce, emerging theater companies to emerge healthily and all theater professionals to understand and best navigate the business of theater.

TRUONLINE.ORG

notes & brainstorming

final words

FROM HOLLY REED

Congratulations! If you've made it to this point, you're a rockstar! I know I've provided you with a lot to think about regarding writing a musical. I hope that it has proven helpful, motivational, and maybe even inspired you to try things you haven't thought of—or had the courage to do—before.

That's my goal.

If I can give just one of you a big push out of your comfort zone and into new territory for you to flourish, then I've succeeded. If you find just one way to better share your gift with the world, it was all worth it.

Here are a few final thoughts.

First, don't worry about being perfect. Weeks, months, and years later, you'll look back at this planner and see how much you've grown. That's GOOD.

Second, know that Rome wasn't built in a year. Better yet—*Hamilton* wasn't written in a year. Lin Manuel Miranda spent over 10 years working on that masterpiece before it had its Broadway debut. Great takes time. Give yourself time.

Third, don't be afraid to ask for help. I have found that in the musical theater industry, people are nice. There's no reason not to ask for advice, direction, and an extra set of eyes if you need it. Many people, including myself, are happy to help out. You'd be surprised! Just ask.

Finally, STAY AWESOME. Just your effort to give this thing a whirl means you're a mover and a shaker and will get it done one way or another.

Don't give up.

Keep chasing your dreams.

You're an inspiration to all who come after.

Holly Reed

I hope you've enjoyed the Ultimate Musical Writer's Planner as much as I loved creating it for you. I can't thank you enough for your continued support of MusicalWriters.com. I appreciate you for purchasing this planner, and if you have an extra second, I would love to hear what you think about it. Please leave a comment at:
www.musicalwriters.com/musical-writers-planner

*If you'd rather say hello on social, I'm @musicalwriters on **Facebook**, **Instagram**, and **Twitter**. Stop by and say hi! Or feel free to send me an email at hollyr@musicalwriters.com.*

Disclaimer

The information contained in this guide is for informational purposes only.

I am not a lawyer or an accountant. Any legal or financial advice that I give is my opinion based on my own experience. You should always seek the advice of a professional before acting on something that I have published or recommended.

Please understand that there are some links contained in this guide that I may benefit from financially.

The material in this guide may include information, products, or services by third parties. Third Party Materials comprise the products and opinions expressed by their owners. As such, I do not assume responsibility or liability for any Third Party material or opinions.

The publication of such Third Party Materials does not constitute my guarantee of any information, instruction, opinion, products, or services contained within the Third Party Material. The use of recommended Third Party Material does not guarantee any success and/or earnings related to you or your musical. Publication of such Third Party Material is simply a recommendation and an expression of my own opinion of that material.

No part of this publication shall be reproduced, transmitted, or sold in whole or in part in any form, without the prior written consent of the author. All trademarks and registered trademarks appearing in this guide are the property of their respective owners.

Users of this guide are advised to do their own due diligence when it comes to making business decisions and all information, products, and services that have been provided should be independently verified by your own qualified professionals. By reading this guide, you agree that myself and my company is not responsible for the success or failure of your business decisions relating to any information presented in this guide.

Made in United States
North Haven, CT
31 May 2022